Elrose Hunter and Simon Smith

Abraham
THE FRIEND OF GOD

Scripture Union
207–209 Queensway, Bletchley, Milton Keynes, MK2 2EB
Email: info@scriptureunion.org.uk
Website: www.scriptureunion.org.uk

Scripture Union Australia
Locked Bag 2, Central Coast Business Centre, NSW 2252
Website: www.scriptureunion.org.au

Scripture Union USA
PO Box 987, Valley Forge, PA 19482
Website: www.scriptureunion.org

British Library Cataloguing-in-Publication Data
A catalogue record of this book is available from the British Library.

Printed and bound by Tien Wah Press, Singapore

Cover design: fourninezero design

Scripture Union is an international charity working with churches in more than 130 countries, providing resources to bring the good news of Jesus Christ to children, young people and families and to encourage them to develop spiritually through the Bible and prayer.

As well as our network of volunteers, staff and associates who run holidays, church-based events and school Christian groups, we produce a wide range of publications and support those who use our resources through training programmes.

Long ago, in a faraway land, God spoke to a man called Abram. God said, "Leave your home and go to the land that I will show you." God made a promise to Abram.

Use the code to find the missing words in God's promise to Abram.

"I will bless you and make your
✓ ❋ ▲ ✗ ❋ ■ ✓ ❀ ■ ▼ ▲

_____

into a great
■ ❀ ▼ ❋ ✐ ■

_____."

a = ❀   e = ❋   o = ✐

c = ✗   i = ❋   s = ▲

d = ✓   n = ■   t = ▼

So Abram, his wife Sarah and his nephew Lot set off on a long journey. They didn't know where their journey would end but Abram trusted God to show him.

Follow the path and use a mirror to unscramble the words to find out what they may have faced on the journey. Join the dots at the end to discover the name of the new land.

Genesis 12:4–9

The journey was long and hard. They lived in tents and took flocks of animals with them. At last God told Abram, "This is the land."

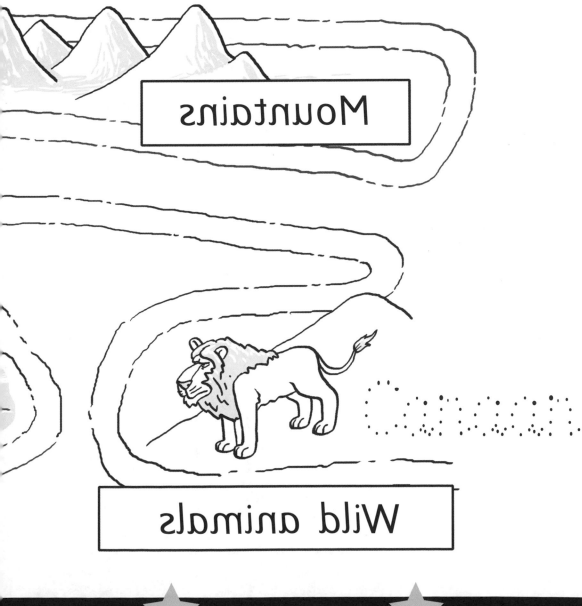

Mountains

Canaan

Wild animals

Abram had flocks of sheep, goats and cattle which needed grass and water. Lot had flocks too and after a while there was not enough grass for the two of them to stay together. Their herdsmen began to quarrel.

Put the words in the right order to find out why they were quarrelling.

"___ ___ __ ___ _____ _____."

well Abram's for sheep is This

Lot's is This flocks for grass

"___ ___ __ __ _____ _____."

At last Abram said to Lot, "Let's separate. You choose the part of the land you want and I'll go the opposite way." So Lot chose the valley beside a river where there was plenty of grass and water for his animals.

Write the first letter of the word for each picture in the centre of the picture wheel to discover the name of the river. Start with the jug and go clockwise.

Time passed. One day a messenger brought bad news to Abram. "There has been a battle near where Lot lives. The enemy has taken away many prisoners. Lot and his family are prisoners too."

Follow the maze to help Abram rescue Lot. Then colour them both!

Abram gathered a band of warriors and they chased the enemy. They attacked at night and rescued Lot and his family and their belongings.

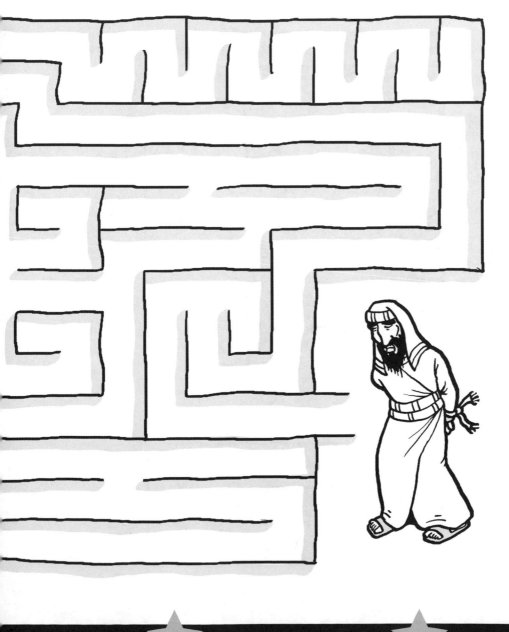

Abram set up his tents near the town of Hebron. One day God said to Abram, "Look at the land around you in all directions. I will give it all to you and your family." "But I don't have any children," Abram replied. "I promise that you will have a son," God said. "Trust me!"

Choose the right jigsaw piece to complete the map of the land.

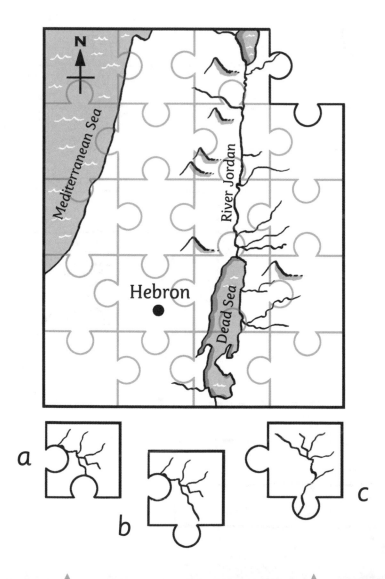

And one night, as Abram stood outside his tent, God said, "Look up! See if you can count the stars. That's how many descendants you will have." Later God also said, "I am changing your name from Abram to Abraham."

Count all the stars you can see in the sky. Find the missing letters to discover the meaning of Abraham. Choose from a,e,i,o.

"F_th_r _f m__ny n_t_ __ns."

Abraham and Sarah were growing old and still they had no children. One hot day Abraham was sitting under a tree near his tent when three men came by. "Please stop and rest here in the shade. I will prepare some food for you," Abraham said. The men sat down gratefully and waited.

Abraham and Sarah made a meal of bread and meat with milk and yogurt. Abraham took the food to the strangers. "Where is your wife, Sarah?" they asked. "In the tent," replied Abraham. "God has a message for Sarah," the men said.

Put the words on the leaves in the right order to work out God's message for Sarah.

Sarah heard what they said and laughed to herself. "I'm too old to have a baby," she thought. But God asked Abraham, "Why did Sarah laugh? I am the Lord! Nothing is too hard for me."

Colour in the picture and find six things that should not be there. Write in three words that describe how Sarah may have felt.

God's promise came true and Sarah had a baby boy. They named him Isaac, which means 'laughter'. Abraham and Sarah were very happy and Isaac grew into a strong boy.

Sarah may have felt

_____

_____

_____

Some years later, God decided to see if Abraham still trusted him. "Take Isaac to a mountain I will show you and offer him as a sacrifice to me," God said. Abraham set off with Isaac, who did not know what God had said. As they walked up the mountain together, Isaac was puzzled and asked his father, "Where is the lamb for the sacrifice?"

Use the code to work out how Abraham answered Isaac's question.

a = ❀ m = ★

b = ☀ o = ✏

d = ✓ p = □

e = ❄ r = ✳

g = ✎ t = ▼

h = ✂ v = ◆

i = ✳ w = ☽

l = ●

When they arrived at the place, Abraham built an altar and laid Isaac on it. He was about to kill his son when God shouted from heaven, "Abraham! Don't hurt your son! Now I know that you trust and love me, because you were willing to offer your only son to me."

Join the dots to find what Abraham offered as a sacrifice to God instead of Isaac.

Abraham lived for more than one hundred years. One day he called his most trusted servant and said to him, "Go back to the land where I was born and find a wife for Isaac. Go to my relatives. God will help you find the right woman." So the servant set off, taking rich gifts with him.

Count the number of camels the servant took with him and put the number in the box. Look carefully at the saddle covers and find two that match. Tick them and colour them in.

Number
of camels

Genesis 24:1–10

When he got near the city where Abraham's brother lived, the servant stopped by a well. It was late afternoon, the time when women came there for water. The servant prayed to God, "Let me find a wife for Isaac today. If I ask a girl for a drink and she offers to get water for my camels as well, I will know she is the one you have chosen." Just then a beautiful girl came by and the servant asked her for a drink.

Follow the letters around the rope to find out what the girl said to the servant.

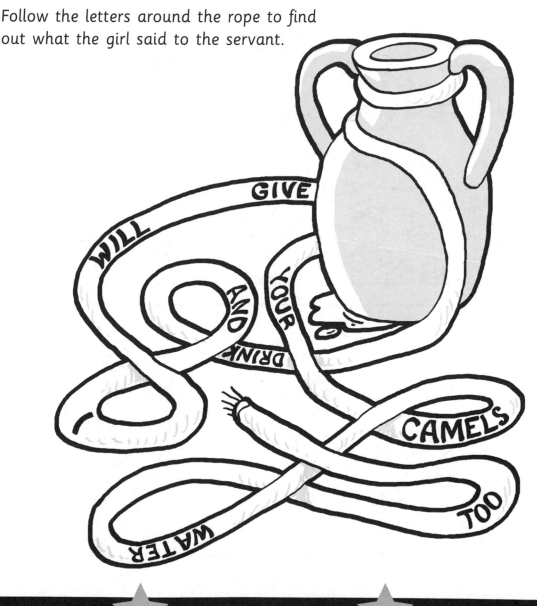

Abraham's servant gave the girl a gold ring and bracelets and she told him that her grandfather was Abraham's brother! "Come and stay at our house," said the girl whose name was Rebekah. The servant thanked God and followed Rebekah home. He told her family his story and they welcomed him with food for himself, the other servants and the camels.

Next day, Rebekah agreed to travel back with Abraham's servant. She brought with her some women servants. They got on camels and said goodbye to the family. When they came near Isaac's home, he came out to meet them. Isaac married Rebekah and loved her dearly.

When you have read both pages, put the pictures in the right order to tell the story. Write the numbers 1 to 4 in the stars. Colour in the pictures.

Years later Isaac and Rebekah had twin boys. They called them Esau and Jacob. As the boys grew up, Esau loved the outdoor life and became a good hunter. His father liked Esau and the meat he brought back from hunting. Jacob became a shepherd and was his mother's favourite son.

How many sheep can you find in this picture?

Genesis 25:19–28

One day when Jacob was cooking some stew, Esau came back from hunting. "I'm starving!" Esau exclaimed. "Give me some of that stew!" Jacob replied, "I will, if you will promise to give me your rights as the firstborn son." "I promise! What use are they to me right now?" said Esau carelessly.

Use the grid to fill in the missing words and find out what Esau gave away.

	1	2	3	4	5
A	b	k	c	x	h
B	j	q	y	i	d
C	t	a	p	w	n
D	g	u	f	s	e
E	m	r	v	l	o

The firstborn son

D1 D5 C1

would __ __ __ most

C3 E2 E5 C3 D5 E2 C1 B3

of his father's __ __ __ __ __ __ __ __

when he died and would become

A5 D5 C2 B5   D3 C2 E1 B4 E4 B3

__ __ __ __ of the __ __ __ __ __ __.

When Isaac grew old he was almost blind. One day he called to Esau, "Go hunting and bring back some good meat. Cook it and I will give you my blessing before I die." So Esau set off with his bow and arrows. Meanwhile, Rebekah called to Jacob, "Quick! Bring me some goats' meat. I will cook it the way your father likes. You can pretend to be Esau and get your father's blessing."

Look in the wordsearch for the words from the story. Put a ring round the words when you find them. Then write out the letters you have left. What do they spell?

BOW
ARROW
MEAT
GOAT
ESAU
JACOB
WILD
FOOD
ANIMAL
BLESSING
HUNTING
TASTY

B	O	W	B	O	C	A	J
L	F	O	O	D	Y	N	W
E	R	R	E	T	B	I	E
S	K	R	S	A	L	M	H
S	A	A	T	D	E	A	N
I	T	A	D	I	S	L	S
N	O	A	M	E	A	T	A
G	N	I	T	N	U	H	C

_ _ _ _ _ _ _ and _ _ _ _ _

"But I'm smooth-skinned and Esau is hairy," Jacob said. "I've thought of that," replied Rebekah. When the food was ready, Jacob took it to his father. "Please eat the meat I have brought. Then give me your blessing," he said. "You sound like Jacob," said Isaac. "Are you really Esau?" "Yes, I am," lied Jacob. So old Isaac ate the food and gave Jacob his blessing.

Look carefully at the picture to see how Jacob tricked his father. Read the jumbled words backwards to complete the sentences.

He wore Esau's s e h t o l c _____.

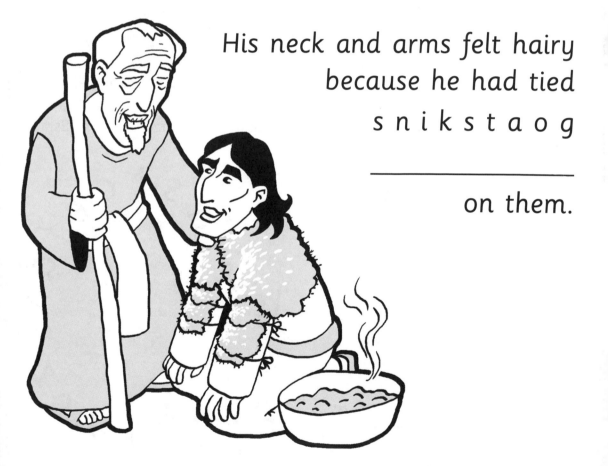

His neck and arms felt hairy because he had tied

s n i k s t a o g

_____

on them.

When Esau came back from hunting, he cooked a tasty meal and took it to his father. "Please eat the meat I have brought and give me your blessing," he said. "Who are you?" asked Isaac, trembling. "Esau, your firstborn son," he answered. "But I've just given my blessing. Your brother tricked me and stole it," Isaac said sadly. From then on Esau hated his brother and said to himself, "I'll kill Jacob after my father dies."

Rebekah, Jacob and Esau did wrong things in this sad story. Follow the trail to find out what they did. Start with p and cross out every other letter to spell out what they did.

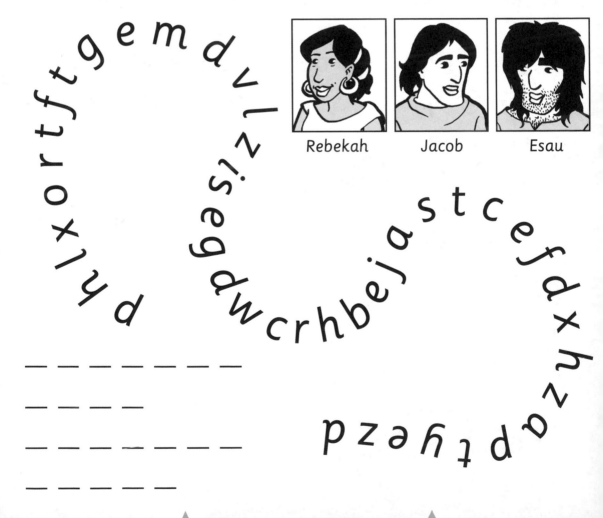

Rebekah   Jacob   Esau

p h l x o r t f t g e m d v l z i s e g d w c r h b e j a s t c e f d x h z a p t y e z d

_ _ _ _ _ _ _ _

_ _ _ _

_ _ _ _ _ _ _

_ _ _ _ _

Rebekah heard of Esau's plan. She said to Jacob, "Go and stay with my brother for a while until Esau cools down." So Jacob set off on the long journey. On the way he lay down to sleep under the stars. He dreamt that he saw a ladder reaching from earth to heaven with angels on it. God was standing beside it and he made a promise to Jacob.

Start at the bottom of the ladder and follow the words up to the top to see what God promised Jacob.

Jacob went to live with his uncle Laban and worked for him as a shepherd. He fell in love with Laban's younger daughter, Rachel, but Laban tricked him into marrying Leah, his elder daughter. However, he later gave him Rachel as well. In those days men could have more than one wife.

Look at these pictures showing Jacob when he left Canaan and when he came back.

Genesis 29

After many years, Jacob returned to Canaan with his wives and children. He had 12 sons, and his favourite son was Joseph. His brother, Esau, forgave him and welcomed him back. Jacob was learning to trust God just as his grandfather Abraham had done.

Find six different things in the second picture that are not in the first. Groups (for example 'children') count as one thing!

Answers

Page 3: descendants, nation

Pages 4–5: Desert, Rivers, Mountains, Wild animals; Canaan

Page 6: "This well is for Abram's sheep."
"This grass is for Lot's flocks."

Page 7: Jordan

Page 10: Piece b

Page 11: 25 stars; Father of many nations

Pages 12–13: "Next year, Sarah will have a son."

Pages 14–15: Toy car, man with headphones, games console, book, man in glasses, electric guitar

Page 16: "God will provide the lamb."

Page 18: Ten camels

Page 19: "Drink, and I will give your camels water too."

Pages 20–21:

Page 22: 11 sheep

Page 23: get, property, head, family

Page 24: Rebekah and Isaac

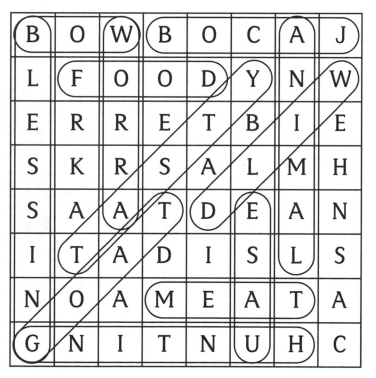

Page 25: clothes, goatskins

Page 26: plotted, lied, cheated, hated

Page 27: "I will protect you. I will bring you back to this land."

Page 28: Wives, children, sheep, goats, cows, donkeys

Discover more Bible stories with these great puzzle books!

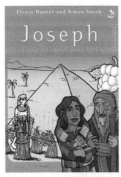

Joseph
The Incredible Dreamer

£2.50
978 1 84427 348 5

Moses
The Brave Leader

£2.50
978 1 84427 075 0

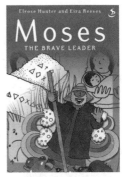

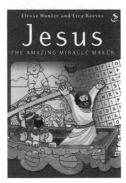

David
The Giant Killer

£2.50
978 1 84427 076 7

Daniel
The Lion Tamer

£2.50
978 1 84427 349 2

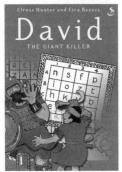

Jesus
The Amazing Miracle Maker

£2.50
978 1 84427 077 4

Peter
The Fisher of Men

£2.50
978 1 84427 350 8

Paul
The Fearless Adventurer

£2.50
978 1 84427 078 1